BASIC/NOT BORING

PHONICS & WORD RECOGNITION
Grades K-1

Inventive Exercises to Sharpen Skills and Raise Achievement

Series Concept & Development
by Imogene Forte & Marjorie Frank
Exercises by Charlotte Poulos

Incentive Publications, Inc.
Nashville, Tennessee

About the cover:
> Bound resist, or tie dye, is the most ancient known method of fabric surface design. The brilliance of the basic tie dye design on this cover reflects the possibilities that emerge from the mastery of basic skills.

Illustrated by Kathleen Bullock
Cover art by Mary Patricia Deprez, dba Tye Dye Mary®
Cover design by Marta Drayton, Joe Shibley, and W. Paul Nance
Edited by Anna Quinn

ISBN 0-86530-383-5

PRINTED IN THE UNITED STATES OF AMERICA

TABLE OF CONTENTS

Appendix

CELEBRATE BASIC LANGUAGE SKILLS

Basic does not mean boring! There is certainly nothing dull about . . .
    . . . helping an octopus figure out beach ball riddles
    . . looking for letters in your alphabet soup
    . . . tracking down words on animal footprints
    . . . searching a picnic basket for tasty vowels
    . . . using words to help rescue a cat from a burning building
    . . . solving puzzles on roller coasters and shooting stars

The idea of celebrating the basics is just what it sounds like—enjoying and improving the skills of reading and using words. Each page of this book invites young learners to try a high-interest, visually appealing exercise that will sharpen one specific phonics or word skill. This is not just any ordinary fill-in-the-blanks way to learn. These exercises are fun and surprising, and they make good use of thinking skills. Students will do the useful work of practicing phonics skills while they enjoy adventures with animals.

The pages in this book can be used in many ways:
- to review or practice a phonics skill with one student
- to sharpen the skill with a small or large group
- to start off a lesson on a particular skill
- to assess how well a student has mastered a skill

Each page has directions that are written simply. It is intended that an adult be available to help students read the information on the page, if help is needed. In most cases, the pages will best be used as a follow-up to a lesson or skill that has already been taught. The pages are excellent tools for immediate reinforcement of a concept.

As your students take on the challenges of these adventures with phonics, they will grow! And as you watch them check off the basic language skills they've acquired or strengthened, you can celebrate with them.

The Skills Test

Use the skills test beginning on page 57 as a pretest and/or a post-test. This will help you check the students' mastery of basic phonics and word skills and will prepare them for success on achievement tests.

SKILLS CHECKLIST
PHONICS & WORD RECOGNITION, GRADES K-1

✔	SKILL	PAGE(S)
	Recognize and discriminate between all letters of the alphabet	10, 11
	Match uppercase to lowercase letters	11
	Recognize common sight words	12–14
	Recognize high-frequency words	14
	Identify and read beginning consonants	10, 12–14, 17–20
	Put words in alphabetical order	10, 13, 18, 20
	Distinguish between consonants and vowels	15, 16
	Identify and read beginning consonant blends	21–25
	Identify and read beginning consonant clusters & digraphs	23–25
	Identify and read medial consonants	26
	Identify and read words with double consonants	27
	Identify and read final consonants	28, 29
	Identify and read final consonant blends and digraphs	30, 31
	Identify and read short vowels	32–36
	Identify and read long vowels in words ending with silent e	37
	Identify and read long vowel sounds (vowel combinations)	38, 40–42
	Identify and read diphthongs (ow, ou)	39
	Identify and read double vowel combinations (oo, ee)	43
	Recognize final y used as a vowel	44
	Identify and read inflectional endings (ed, ing)	45, 46
	Use phonics to read whole words	12–14, 47–56
	Identify and discriminate between homonyms	48, 49
	Identify nouns	50
	Identify and read proper nouns	51
	Identify and read plural nouns	52
	Identify and read contractions	53
	Identify and read compound words	54, 55
	Identify, read, and use rhyming words	56

PHONICS & WORD RECOGNITION
Grades K-1

Skills Exercises

The Amazing ABC Mole Maze

Max and Matt are exploring a new tunnel.

Color the path in ABC order to help them find their way to a big surprise!

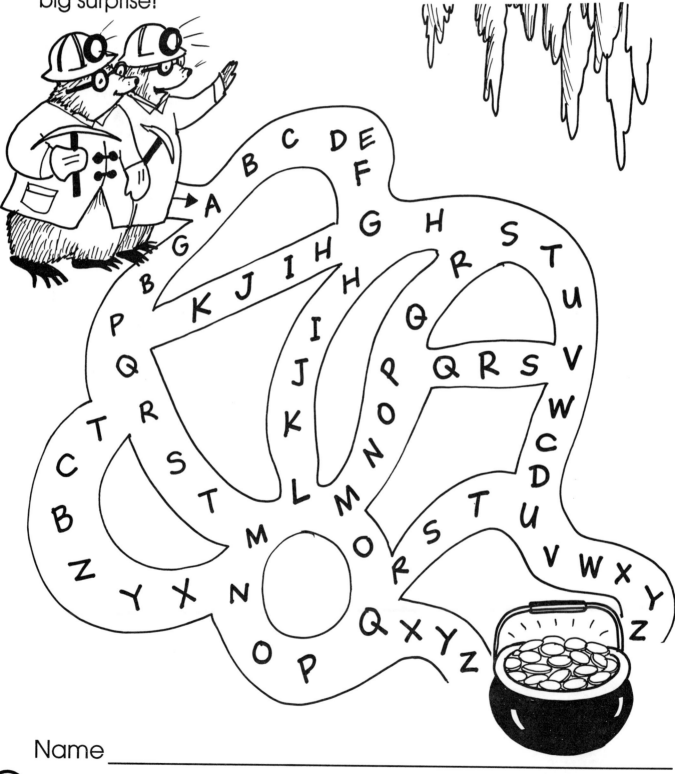

Name _____

ABC Order • Letter Discrimination

Basic Skills/Phonics K-1

Silly Soup

Bernie Bear is about to eat a bowl of letters.

What a funny kind of soup!

Draw a line to match each capital letter with its lowercase letter.

Color the picture.

Name _____

Upper- & Lowercase

Ski Trouble

Oops! Poor Stella Squirrel has lost her ski.

Help her find it by coloring only the boxes that contain real words.

When you are finished, Stella will see a path to her lost ski.

stop	map	shut	twig
rif	moke	ses	ten
sark	twim	rope	sred
koj	make	pute	gik
shaz	fire	sees	star

Name _____

Basic Skills/Phonics K-1

An ABC Adventure

Molly Mouse is having a great adventure.
Connect the dots in ABC order to find out
what Molly is doing.

• hot

it • ——— • gum

jet •

kit • ——————————————— • fox

lid •

mop • ——————————————— • egg

nod

YO-HO-HO

on •

red •

pot   cop

• did

• an   Start

quack big

top

van

x-ray

yes

sun   up   win   zip

Color the picture.

Name _____

Sight Words • ABC Order

13

Who Can See the Wind?

Can you see the wind?
Ted and Joe watch the wind play with their kite.
Read the story and choose words from the **Word Box** to fill in the blanks.
Write the words into the correct places in the kite puzzle.

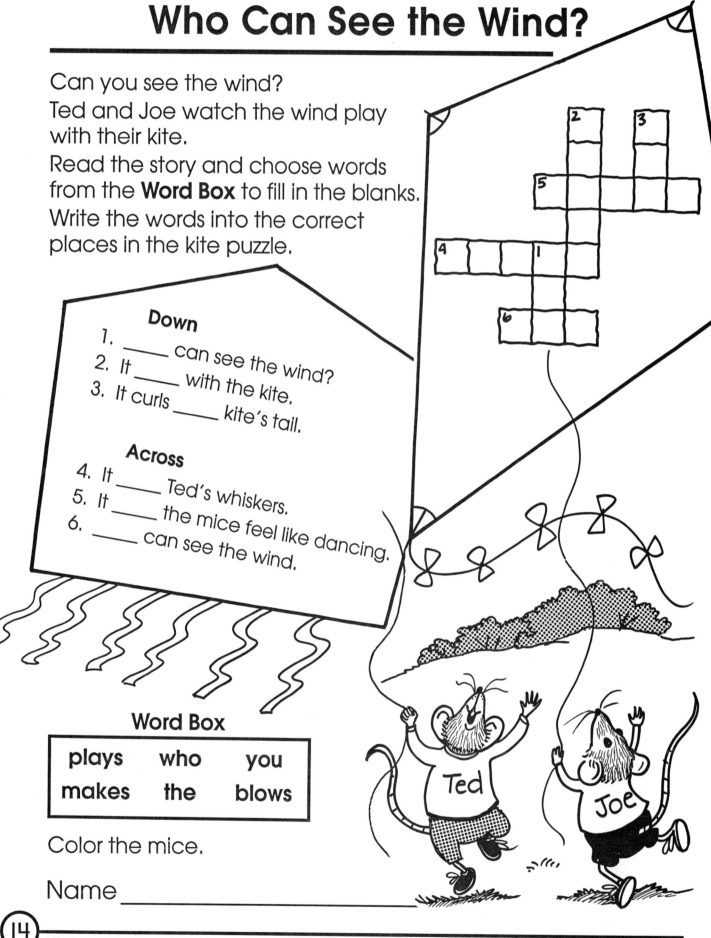

Down

1. _____ can see the wind?
2. It _____ with the kite.
3. It curls _____ kite's tail.

Across

4. It _____ Ted's whiskers.
5. It _____ the mice feel like dancing.
6. _____ can see the wind.

Word Box

plays	who	you
makes	the	blows

Color the mice.

Name _____

Underground Dinner

Misty Mole is ready for dinner.

To help her find the vegetables in her garden, color only the spaces that have consonants.

Do not color the spaces that have vowels.

Name _____

Distinguish Consonants & Vowels

Make a Quilt

You can help Deb and Darla make a beautiful quilt.

Use your **blue** crayon to color each space that has a **vowel.**

Use your **red** crayon to color each space that has a **consonant.**

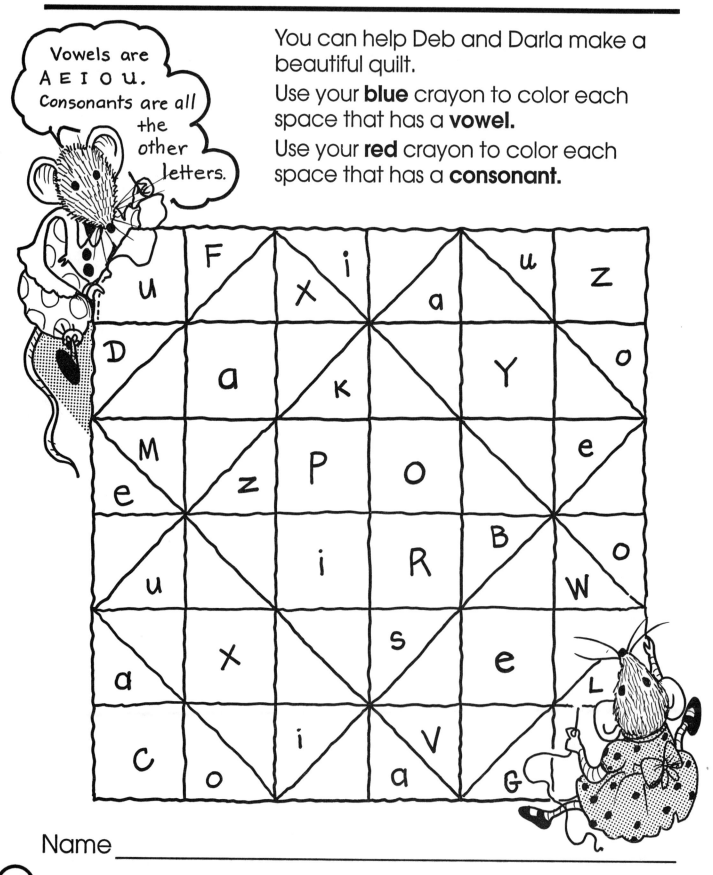

Name _____

Distinguish Consonants & Vowels

Basic Skills/Phonics K-1

Hello! Hello!

Some furry friends are talking.

Each animal is saying the names of things that begin like his own name.

Find 3 things in the picture that begin with the same sound as **bear** and **bunny.**

Color them **brown.**

Find 3 things that begin with the same sound as **fox.**

Color them **orange.**

Find 3 things that begin with the same sound as **squirrel.**

Color them **blue.**

Name _____

Beginning Consonants

A Funny Dream

1. ☐ear
2. ☐og
3. ☐rog
4. ☐iraffe
5. ☐en
6. ☐angaroo
7. ☐ebra
8. ☐ion
9. ☐onkey

In Moose Matt's dream, he saw a parade of animals.

Each animal's name began with a different consonant.

Can you add the correct beginning consonant to each name?

The animals marched in ABC order — except for one.

Circle the animal that is out of order.

Color all the animals.

Name_____

Beginning Consonants

Copyright ©1998 by Incentive Publications, Inc., Nashville, TN.

Basic Skills/Phonics K-1

What a Mess!

Did you ever see such a room?

It is so messy, Jake cannot find his things!

Find 2 things that begin with the letter **T**.
Color them **blue.**

Find 2 things that begin with the letter **B**.
Color them **green.**

Find 1 thing that begins with the letter **K**.
Color it **red.**

Find 1 thing that begins with the letter **P**.
Color it **yellow.**

Name _____

Beginning Consonants

Fire! Fire!

Help! Callie Cat's house is on fire!

Write the mixed-up words on the ladder in ABC order.

Then Callie can use the ladder to get away quickly.

alarm

burn

climb

hot

gray

dog

fire

exit

1. alarm
2.
3.
4.
5.
6.
7.
8.

Color the pictures.

Name _____

Hopping Frogs

Trace the letters that are consonant blends.
Then read the story to find out how to color the picture.
Circle the color word in the story that is silly.

Happy green frogs hop over

a blue creek.

Bright red flowers peek up

from the brown ground.

Gray clouds blow blue rain

down on the pink grass.

Name _____

Basic Skills/Phonics K-1   **Beginning Frog Consonant Blends** (br, cr, fr, gr, bl, cl)

Surf's Up!

What fun for Sammy!

He slips and slides on the waves.

Use the blends in each box to finish the group of words below that box.

| gl | cr | br |

1. ____ eep

2. ____ itter

3. ____ ight

| dr | gr | bl |

4. ____ ay

5. ____ y

6. ____ ue

| pl | fr | fl |

7. ____ ay

8. ____ eeze

9. ____ ip

Color the picture.

Name _____

Beginning Consonant Blends

Beach Ball Riddles

Ollie Octopus wants to know if you can solve his
beach ball riddles.

Each ball is filled with picture clues.

What is the first letter in the name of each picture?

Write it on the correct line near each ball.

You will discover three things that belong in the ocean!

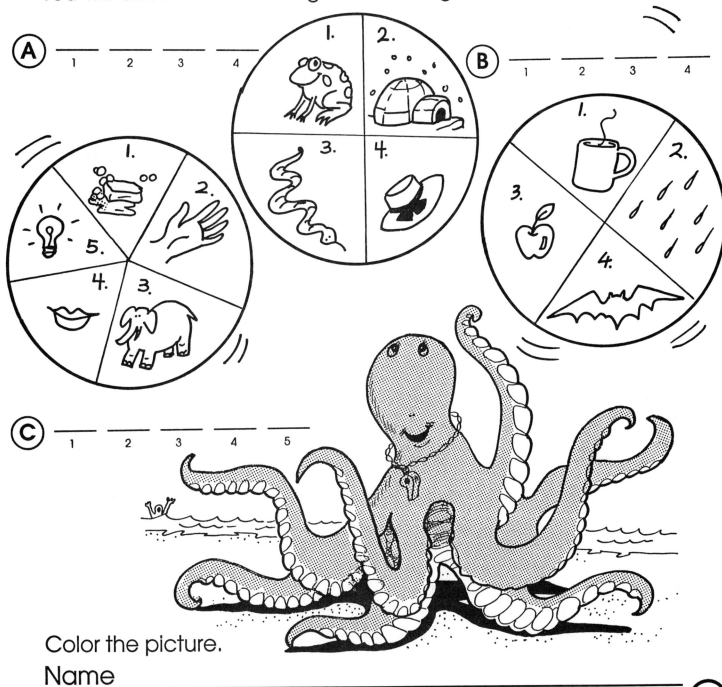

Color the picture.

Name

Beginning Consonants, Blends, & Digraphs

Tricky Tongue Twisters

Busy Billy Blackbird is making tricky tongue twisters. You can, too!
In each group of word pairs, circle the words that begin with the same sound.

To make funny tongue twisters, write the words you circled together on a line.

Write the words from the clouds on line 1.
Write the words from the kites on line 2.
Write the words from the flying disks on line 3.

1.
think
time

tub
thick

tree
thumbs

2.
witch
white

whale
west

watch
wheels

wrong
whistle

3.
chocolate
club

chair
cake

clock
chip

chain
croak

1. _____

2. _____

3. _____

Can you draw pictures of your silly sentences?
Name _____

Beginning Digraphs (th, wh, ch)

Copyright ©1998 by Incentive Publications, Inc., Nashville, TN.
Basic Skills/Phonics K-1

Snow School

Pipi and Pete Penguin go to snow school.
Help them read some words they are
learning at school.

Use the words in the **Word Box** to
label each picture.

2. _____

1. school

3. _____

4. _____

Word Box

school
snowman
sled
square
skates
scarf

5. _____

6. _____

Color the picture.

Name _____

Beginning Blends & Clusters (sc, sk, sl, sn, squ, sch)

A Day in the Desert

What things share the desert home with Louie Lizard?
Look at the name under each picture.
Find the missing letter in the box.
Write the missing letter in the
middle of each word.

1. de__ert

4. tee__ee

5. flo__er

p n s d b w z

2. po__y

6. li__ard

3. sha__ow

7. ro__in

Color the pictures.

Name _____

Medial Consonants

Riddle-Dee-Dee

Olly and Dolly Owl are trying to solve some riddles.
Help them choose a word from the **Word Box** that will answer each riddle.
All the words have double letters.
Write each answer on the line.
Circle the double letters in your answer.
Then draw and color a picture of each answer.

1. I make noise, but I am not alive.

   Babies like to play with me.

   I am a _____.

2. I am soft. I hop.

   I have long ears.

   I am a _____.

3. I grow on trees.

   I am good to eat.

   I am nature's toothbrush.

   I am an _____.

4. I appear after a rain.

   Kids love to play with me.

   I splash on their feet.

   I am a _____.

Word Box

rattle   bunny   puddle   apple

Name _____

Double Consonants

Dan's Dogs

All the neighborhood dogs love Dan.

When Dan runs, all the dogs try to sneak into his pack.

Watch out for pretenders!

Clue: All Dan's dogs have names that end with a vowel.

> Vowels are a, e, i, o, u, and sometimes y.

Color only Dan's dogs.

Name _____

Tic Tac Toe

Tommy Tiger loves to play Tic Tac Toe.
Play some games with Tommy.
Look at each game.
Draw a line to connect 3 things that have the same ending sound.

Name _____

Ellie Is a Puzzle

No one knows much about Ellie.
Ellie is like a big secret.
Read each word scattered on the page.
Then write the words in their correct spaces in the puzzle.
The word that appears in the boxes will tell you who Ellie really is!
Trace Ellie's picture with a purple crayon.

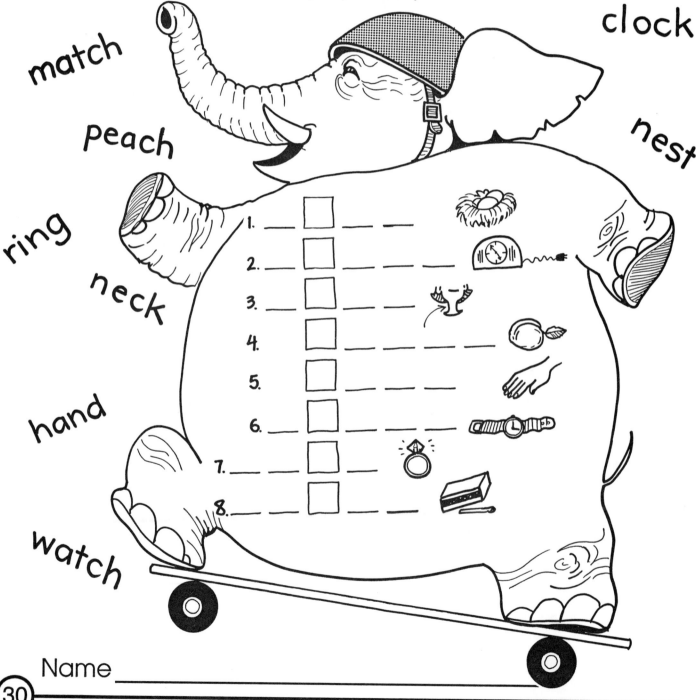

match

clock

peach

nest

ring

neck

hand

watch

1. _____
2. _____
3. _____
4. _____
5. _____
6. _____
7. _____
8. _____

Name _____

Final Blends & Digraphs (ch, ck, nd, ng, st)

Whose Footprints?

Find the prints that belong to each animal.

Ralph Raccoon has all words that end in **ng.**

   Draw a **blue** line to follow his prints.

Robbie Rabbit has all words that end in **tch.**

   Draw an **orange** line to follow her prints.

Darla Deer has all words that end in **sh.**

   Draw a **yellow** line to follow her prints.

Missy Mouse has all words that end in **th.**

   Draw a **brown** line to follow his prints.

   Read aloud the words on each animal's path.

Name _____

Final Blends & Digraphs (ng, sh, th, tch)

Off to Africa!

Anna Banana and Robbie Bobba are going on a safari.
Help them pack.
In Anna's trunk, draw the things with a **short a** sound (like hat).
In Robbie's trunk, draw the things with a **short o** sound (like hot).

Anna Banana

apple

clock

sock

doll

hat

Robbie Bobba

fan

dog

map

can

Color the pictures.

Name _____

Short Vowels (a and o)

Basic Skills/Phonics K-1

Bird Watcher

Kitty is a bird watcher.

Today she has found no birds.

She has spotted some funny things.

Look for 10 hidden pictures.

Color hidden things that have a **short i** sound (like pig) red.

Color hidden things that have a **short u** sound (like mud) green.

Name _____

Short Vowels (i and u)

A Secret Message

A short "e" is like the "e" in bed.

Detective Derby needs help reading a secret message.

Look at the words in the puzzle.

Color in each block with a **short e** word.

You will find a secret message.

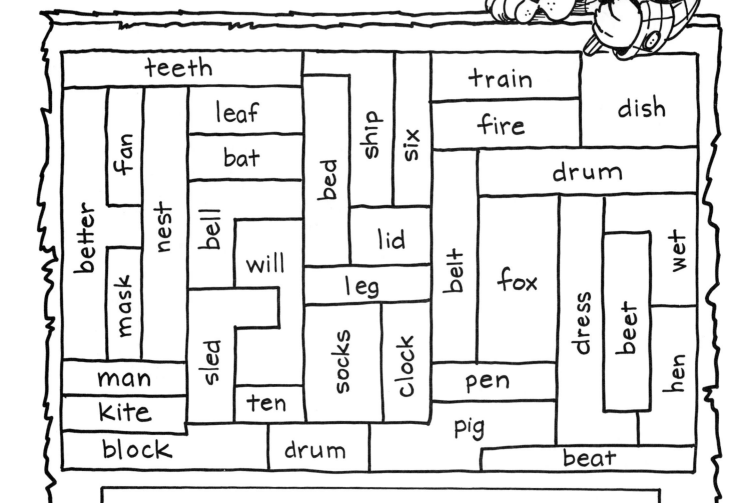

Write the secret message here.

_____

- - - - - - - - - - - - - - - - - - -

_____

Name _____

Short Vowel (e)

Basic Skills/Phonics K-1

Animal Scramble

The animals have lost their names in the pond.

Can you put the scrambled letters in order?

Write each name by the correct animal.

The animals say, "Thank you."

Color the animals and the pond.

Name _____

Short Vowels (a, e, i, o)

A Secret in a Pocket

Roy Raccoon is on his way to the fishing hole.

Can you guess what he has in his pocket?

Write a missing vowel in each word.
(Use **a, e, i, o,** or **u.**)

1. c ☐ t 1.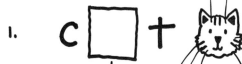

2. c ☐ P 2.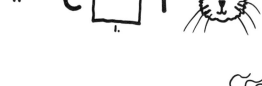

4. P ☐ g 4.

3. n ☐ t 3.

5. P ☐ t 5.

To find Roy's secret, match the numbers and write the missing letters in the spaces below.

What is in Roy's pocket?

_ b _ n c h _ f w _ t
1.   2.   5.   3.

w _ g g l y w _ r m s
4.   5.

Name _____

Short Vowels (a, e, i, o, u)

Words Take a Ride

Five **silent e** words are riding the roller coaster.

What a silly thing for words to do!

Can you add letters to find the word in each car?

Use the words hidden in the **Word Puzzle.**

Color the words you find in the **Word Puzzle.**

Word Puzzle

F	C	A	K	E
I	Z	B	I	F
R	S	I	T	A
E	P	K	E	C
X	W	E	Q	E

Name _____

Silent e

Yummm-Yum!

Look at all the good things in the picnic basket.
Which foods have names with a long vowel sound?
Color everything in the picnic basket whose name has a **long** vowel sound.

Remember that a long vowel says its name as in rake or seed.

Name _____

Make Way for a Worm

Help Wanda Worm find her way through the apple.

Use your crayon to follow the line of words that contain the same vowel sound that you hear in **mouse** and **owl.**

Watch out for Wanda when she gets through the apple.

Don't step on her if she drops out!

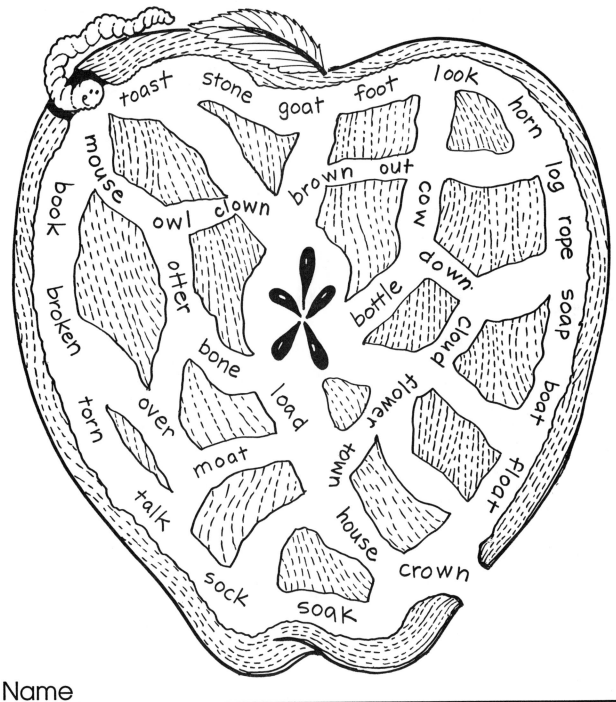

Name _____

Diphthongs (ow, ou)

The Big Blow

Hang on!

There's a big wind blowing.

Everything is going crazy.

Color **only** the things whose names have **long** vowel sounds.

Can you find 10 things?

Hint: The words **cape, beet, rice, blow,** and **flute** have long vowel sounds.

Name _____

Long Vowel Combinations

Basic Skills/Phonics K-1

I Spy

Olly Owl can see 6 animals with his spyglass.

Trace each animal with a different color.

Then use the **Word Box** to help you write the name of each animal.

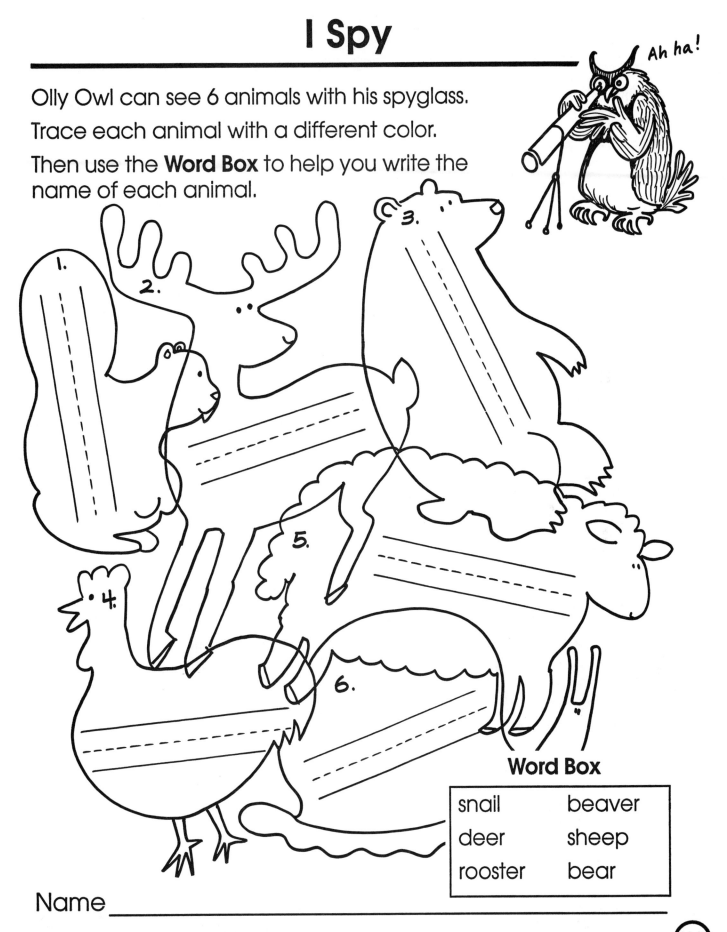

Word Box

snail	beaver
deer	sheep
rooster	bear

Name _____

Long Vowel Combinations

Silly Questions

Read each silly question aloud to yourself.
Underline each word that has a long vowel sound.
Then circle the answer **yes** or **no**.

1. Can a seal cook toast ?
Yes   No

2. Can you eat a boat ?
Yes   No

3. Can a toad hop down a road ?
Yes   No

4. Can a bee sleep on the moon ?
Yes   No

5. Can a mouse sleep in a house ?
Yes   No

6. Can a tree read a book ?
Yes   No

7. Will a boot have a room at the zoo ?
Yes   No

8. Can a coat eat a goat ?
Yes   No

Name _____

Long Vowel Combinations

Double the Fun

Each goofy animal has a double **o** or **e** in its name.
Write a word from **Box 1** on the first line in the bubble to name each animal.
You can make the animals say goofy things!
Write a word from **Box 2** on the second line inside the bubble to show what each animal will say.

1.

2.

3.

4.

Read aloud all the words in the boxes. Listen to the vowel sounds.

Color the animals.

Box 1	Box 2
sheep	Boo!
goose	Shoo!
bee	Ooh!
moose	Zoom!
	Eek!
	Toot!
	Beep!
	Coo!
	See!
	Look!

Name _____

Double Vowels

Funny Bunny

Funny Bunny is caught in a cloud of bubbles.
Read the word on each bubble.
Y is a consonant, but sometimes it acts like a vowel.
If **y** sounds like the **long e** at the end of **puppy**, color the bubble **yellow**.
If **y** sounds like the **long i** at the end of **dry**, color the bubble **red**.

buy

messy

pony

pretty

tiny

cry

candy

city

why

try

bunny

my

fry

baby

scary

smelly

fly

Name _____

Final y

Falling Leaves

Autumn is a favorite time for storytelling.

When the autumn leaves fall, sometimes endings fall off words in a story.

Read the story.

Put **ed** or **ing** back on the words that have lost their endings.

Josh and Judy were go ____ on a walk.

The leaves were fall ____ from the trees.

They walk ____ in the leaves.

Leaves float ____ down.

"Jump!" shout ____ Terry.

"Keep jump ____ in the piles of leaves."

Judy jump ____ and jump____.

"Kick!" yell ____ Judy. "Kick and roll."

Terry kick ____ and roll ____ in the falling leaves.

The leaves swirl ____ in the wind.

"We are hav ____ great fun!" they said.

Color the leaves.

Name _____

Copyright ©1998 by Incentive Publications, Inc., Nashville, TN.
Basic Skills/Phonics K-1

Inflectional Endings (ed & ing)

Winter or Summer?

Pete likes summer fun.
Polly likes winter fun.
Draw a line from Pete to the things he can do in **summer.**
Draw a line from Polly to the things she can do in **winter.**

1. throwing beach balls

2. sailing

3. fishing

4. skiing

5. sledding

6. diving

7. skating

8. biking

9. throwing snowballs

10. making snowmen

Color Pete **brown** or **black.** Color Polly **white.**
Write the name of your favorite season.

Name _____

Inflectional Ending (ing)

Basic Skills/Phonics K-1

Shooting Stars

Andy and Mandy are watching shooting stars.
Read the pairs of words in the picture.
If the two words have the **same** meaning, color that space **blue.**
If the two words are **opposites**, color that space **yellow.**

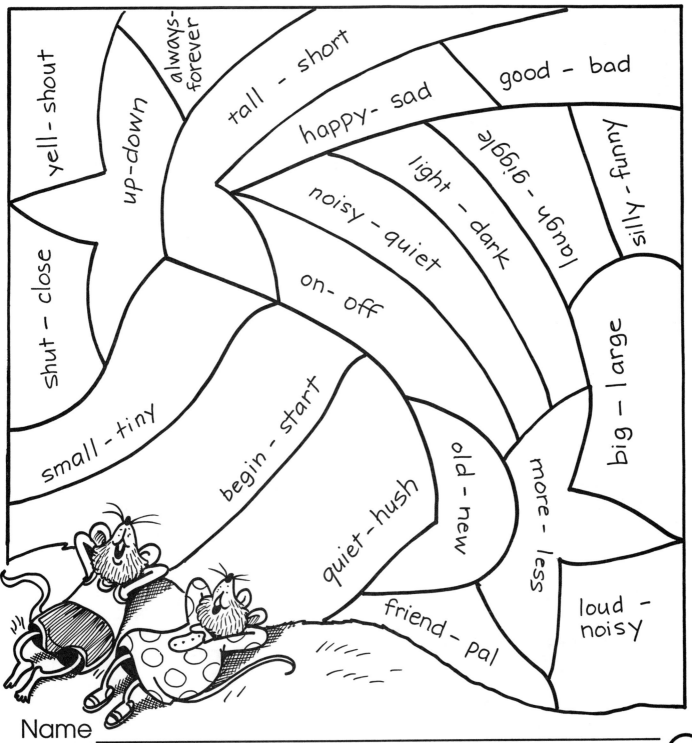

Name _____

Synonyms & Antonyms

Crazy Pictures

Some words sound the same and look the same but mean different things.

Help Morton Mouse draw some crazy pictures.

He wants to draw 2 things for 1 word.

Follow the directions to find out about some of these crazy words!

1. Draw a fancy bow on the bow.

2. Draw a flying bat on the bat.

3. Draw a car parked in the park.

4. Can Elmo put two trunks in the trunk of the car? **Yes**   **No**

I don't think he can.

Color the pictures.

Name _____

Multiple Meanings

Art in the Park

Cool Cat is having an art fair.

He wants his artist friends to join him.

Look at each picture. Read the first word.

Read the second word that sounds the **same** but is spelled **differently.**

Draw a picture to match the second word.

The people in the park will enjoy your artwork.

see   sea

pair   pear

aunt   ant

son   sun

ate   eight

Color the pictures.

Name _____

Nouns on the Line

Naming words are called nouns. Nouns name people, animals, things, and places.

Help Blue Bird line up some nouns.

Fill each space below with pictures of nouns.

Draw 3 animals, 3 people, 3 things, and 3 places.

animals

people

things

places

Name _____

Basic Skills/Phonics K-1

Make It Proper

Help! Some names are missing from the signs!
Choose a proper noun from the **Name Box** to fill in each space.
Be sure to begin each word with a capital letter.

> A proper noun is a special name for a person, place, or thing. It always begins with a capital letter.

1.

(DO NOT FEED ANIMALS)

2.

3 miles

3. It's a party for:

4.
Sam Smith
17 Green St.
Smalltown, U.S.A

Send To:

5. Camp

Name Box

Fish Lake	Camp Pine Tree	Mark Brown
City Zoo	Santa Claus; North Pole	

Name _____

Copyright ©1998 by Incentive Publications, Inc., Nashville, TN.
Basic Skills/Phonics K-1

Proper Nouns

One or More Than One?

The sea creatures are swimming with some underwater nouns.

Read the nouns on each picture.

Three of the nouns on each picture are plural.

Put an **X** on the noun in each picture that is not plural.

Plural nouns name more than one of something, like boats or fins.

masks fins
shells boat

snails
clam
rocks
crabs

bubbles
flippers
tanks

prize

ships eels sharks whale

Make your own set of four nouns.
Make them all plural.

Name _____

Plural Nouns

Basic Skills/Phonics K-1

Let's Go Hiking!

Let's go hiking with Henry.

First, we will have to help him lace up his boots.

Draw a line from each pair of words to its contraction.

Contractions are 2 words squeezed into 1.
I am = I'm
You will = You'll

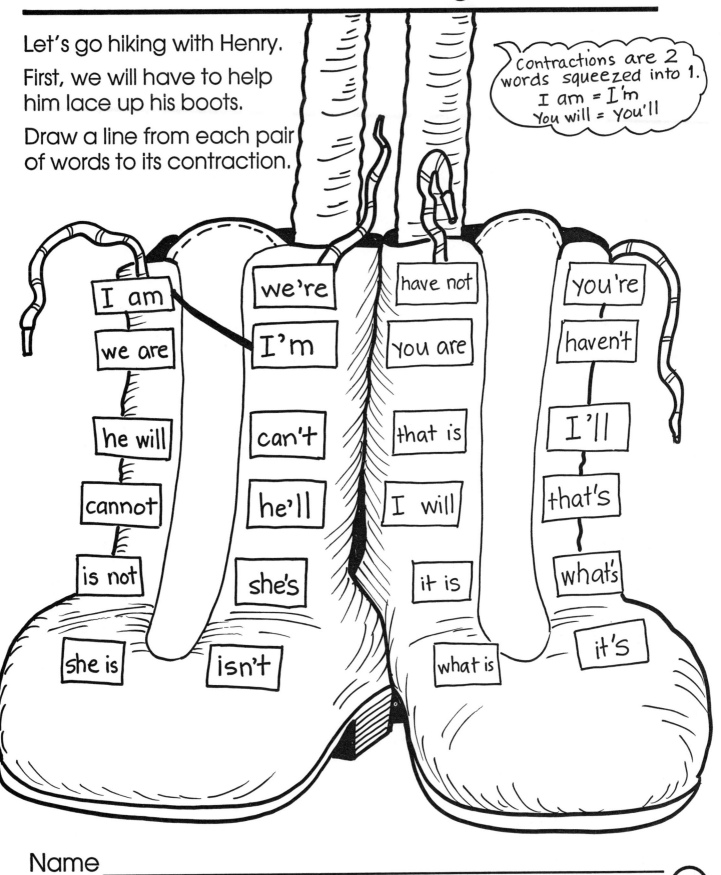

I am	we're
we are	I'm
he will	can't
cannot	he'll
is not	she's
she is	isn't

have not	you're
you are	haven't
that is	I'll
I will	that's
it is	what's
what is	it's

Name _____

Petal Puzzles

Help Betty Beetle solve the picture puzzles on this flower.
Write a **compound word** for each picture puzzle.
Make the compound words from words in the **Word Box.**

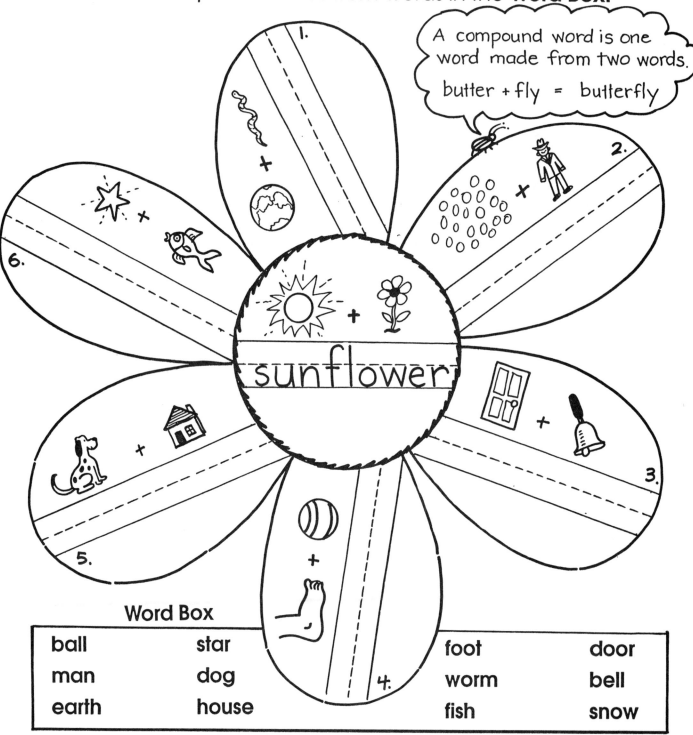

A compound word is one word made from two words.

butter + fly = butterfly

Word Box

ball	star	foot	door
man	dog	worm	bell
earth	house	fish	snow

Name _____

Compound Words

Flying Freddy

Did you ever fly on a **compound word?**

Trace the words to show the compound word Freddy is flying on.

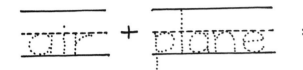

air + plane = airplane

Choose 2 words from the **Word Box** to make a compound word for each of these.

1. Make a compound word you can eat.

   _____

2. Make a compound word you can use for a game.

   _____

3. Make a compound word you can use to grow flowers.

   _____

4. Make a compound word you can use to clean your teeth.

   _____

Word Box

base	corn	ball	tooth
green	pop	house	brush

Name _____

Balloons to the Moon!

It's a race to the moon.
Who will win—the rat or the goat?
Look at the pictures on the balloons.
Draw lines to connect any 2 or 3 whose names **rhyme.**

Who will get here first ? A fat rat in a flat hat, or a goat in a coat with a boat ?

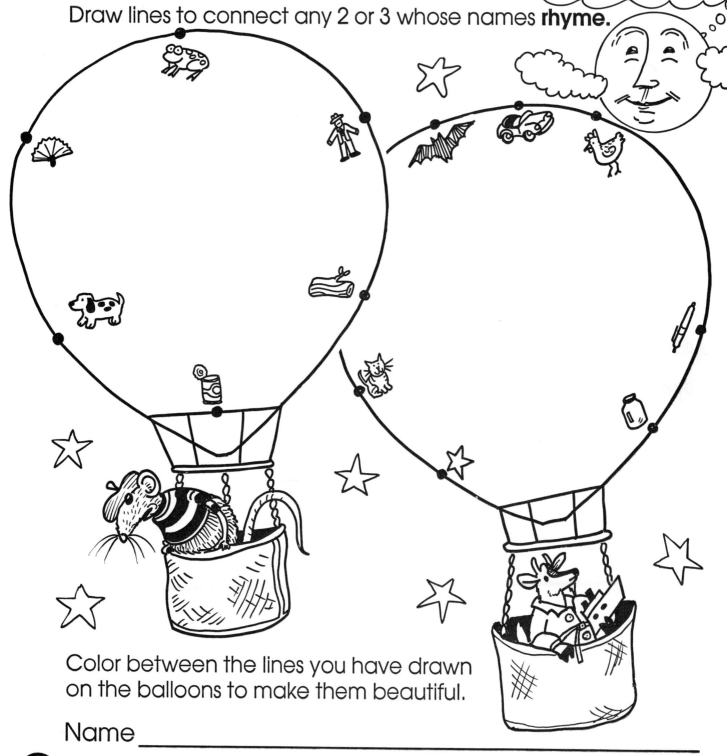

Color between the lines you have drawn on the balloons to make them beautiful.

Name _____

Rhyming Words

Basic Skills/Phonics K-1